To Sue, Jenny + Family,

Thankyou all for the wonderful
times with you at Katy's 21st.
Do come + visit us soon.

Lots of love,

Jan xox

FARM COUNTRY

Panoramic photography of rural New Zealand

Andris Apse

CRAIG
POTTON
PUBLISHING

Farmland near Fairlie, South Canterbury, showing Ben McLeod Range

INTRODUCTION

New Zealand is unique among developed countries in relying for the major part of its export earnings on agriculture, horticulture, fishing and forestry. All other developed countries have a substantial manufacturing or mining base, but New Zealand's wealth comes from grass, trees, water and soil. The development in New Zealand of pastoral farming and fruit growing over nearly 200 years of European settlement has produced world-leading dairy, sheep, deer, apple and kiwifruit industries. It has also resulted in leadership positions in strong wool, grass-fed beef and grape growing for sauvignon blanc, chardonnay and pinot noir varieties.

The primary industries include softwood and paper pulp from large-scale, fast-growing exotic forests, mainly *Pinus radiata*, and high-quality seafood from ocean species and inshore aquaculture on marine farms. All of these industries combine to produce over 60 per cent of annual export earnings as well as satisfying the New Zealand population of four million, plus two million tourists annually. All food and fibre products have a reputation for being of the highest quality, safe to eat and fit-for-purpose. New Zealand has never had some of the major animal and poultry diseases, like foot-and-mouth, bovine spongiform encephalitis (BSE), Newcastle disease or avian influenza. Isolated from other countries by huge stretches of ocean, New Zealand has a strict biosecurity regime, which incoming travellers encounter at airports, and the highest food inspection standards for export and domestic produce.

The reputation for high quality begins in the New Zealand environment, with abundant clean air and water, a long coastline, plenty of native vegetation and the right temperate climate for growth almost all year round. Farmers and orchardists build on this platform to produce excellence in dairy products, meat, cereals, fruit and vegetables. They are members of many quality assurance and environmental awareness schemes, actively restoring any damage or unsustainable business practices which may have been introduced.

In a ground-breaking report in 2004 called *Growing for Good; Intensive Farming, Sustainability and New Zealand's Environment*, the Parliamentary Commissioner for the Environment drew attention to some over-use of groundwater supplies and of nitrogenous fertilisers, which may pollute the waterways and lakes in the future.

The report called for the redesign of farming systems to emphasise the extensive, low-input, pasture-only approach which was developed here and has proven so successful. It added that intensive farming carries big environmental and financial risks which New Zealand is young and smart enough as a country to avoid.

This message was well received, because it matched the aspirations of New Zealand producers, as well as our economic circumstances. The ambition of every New Zealand farmer is to pass on the land to future generations in better condition than he or she inherited it. The reputation for food quality in European, North American and Asian supermarkets brings good financial rewards for New Zealand's food producers, along with extra responsibilities. These include trace-back systems, animal health vigilance, integrated pest management and verifiable environmental standards, in addition to the very best eating quality and presentation.

The emphasis on premium food exporting unites the supply chain, from farm to retail store, instead of making one farmer or processor compete against another to drive down prices. But that production must be carried out on a low-cost input base, because New Zealand is thousands of kilometres from its markets, where local foods will have consumer loyalty and less food-miles load.

However, many Northern Hemisphere producers do not have the economies of scale and low-cost farming methods enjoyed by New Zealanders. They take livestock indoors during harsh winters, and cope with urban encroachment, herbicide resistance, polluted water supplies and exhausted soil structure. The trend to high-input farming, with big machinery, expensive genetics and costly fuel bills, has left those farmers with unsustainable businesses, reliant on non-farm income, incentives and subsidies.

It doesn't have to be that way in New Zealand though, as the Parliamentary Commissioner for the Environment said in his report. During the 1970s and 80s there was a time when New Zealand was seduced by the concept of price support for farmers. Guaranteed prices would help farming avoid boom and bust periods and underpin the national economy,

so the argument went. But a small economy of $100 billion gross domestic product cannot hope to subsidise the export returns of its largest sector, exposed to world demand-supply influences and the value of the New Zealand dollar against other currencies. So in 1984 state support, in various forms, was cut off from New Zealand farmers and they now live on pure market prices, plus the fluctuations of dollar value. New Zealand has the smallest state support level for agriculture, less than 1 per cent of farm gate output value, compared with 40 per cent or more in some heavily protected countries like Japan, Canada, the US and the EU.

Philosophically, New Zealand farmers and orchardists would not have it any other way. Market exposure encourages innovation, keeps down costs and demands land-use changes if returns stay persistently low in one farming type. Diversification options and family farm ownership with high equity levels also contribute to the viability of New Zealand farming.

In the spirit of openness which characterises farmers the world over, New Zealand's primary sector does not believe in keeping secret the knowledge and tools it has developed to make farming, horticulture and forestry more efficient and productive.

For instance, New Zealand pioneered the commercial growing of kiwifruit, formerly the Chinese gooseberry, and this fruit is now found in commercial quantities in many countries of the world. But it is in the major pastoral industries of dairying, sheep, beef and deer farming, that New Zealand common sense and ingenuity has come up with farming systems, machinery and software which will be useful to farmers around the world. The export of New Zealand agricultural technology earns over $600 million annually. In some parts of Europe and the United States a back-to-basics revolution in farming has resulted from exposure to New Zealand ways and ideas. So what are these basics of farming in New Zealand which justify the claim to be 'clean, green and unique'?

LOCATION

New Zealand has a wonderful climate suitable for agriculture and horticulture, lying in southern temperate zone latitudes, with 15,000 kilometres of coastline and a westerly influenced maritime climate. This means temperatures get neither too hot nor too cold, and pasture grows all year round in the north and for eight to nine months in the south. The mean annual sea-level temperature varies from 15°C in the north to 9°C in the south. Summer daytime temperatures range between 15°C and 30°C and zero to 15°C in the winter. Most regions of the country receive at least 1500 millimetres of rainfall annually, well distributed throughout the year.

The total land area of New Zealand is 27.1 million hectares, the same size as Japan. However, New Zealand has only 4 million people, and pastoral farming and horticulture extends over 13.5 million hectares, more than 80 per cent of the occupied area and nearly half of the total land area. There are 24,000 sheep and beef farms, 13,000 dairy farms, 2000 deer farms, 1500 arable farms and about 10,000 orchards. In the 2001 Census 500,000 people identified themselves as living in rural areas, with about 150,000 working full or part-time, paid or unpaid, in agriculture and horticulture. The same number again is employed in agricultural servicing industries like meat processing, road transport and rural merchandising.

DEVELOPMENT

New Zealand's position in the south-west corner of the Pacific Ocean was a challenge to early Maori and European explorers, but when they arrived after weeks of travel they found a verdant land with abundant bird and fish species, and no land mammals. Food was plentiful for the early settlers, unlike in neighbouring Australia, which is an arid land. Maori grew kumara, a sweet potato, and quickly turned to market gardening when the first European arrivals brought fruit and vegetable seeds from England. Many of the first Europeans were farmers from England and Scotland, keen to grow grain, plant fruit trees and establish pastures for their livestock. Large tracts of native forest were felled and burned so that grass seeds could be sown into the ash and exposed soil. Fences were built to keep livestock within the boundaries of the new farms, and better bulls and rams were bred to improve the herds and flocks. The techniques of ploughing, sowing, shepherding, animal breeding and dairy cow management came from the Home Country settlers, who had inherited centuries of farming knowledge and skills.

It wasn't long before a uniquely New Zealand way of farming emerged however. This country was generally productive because the grass grew for longer during the year in the temperate climate, and plants and animals were not at first exposed to pests and diseases, although these did come along later. The basic lack of soil fertility after the boost from the ash meant that farms needed to be bigger to be viable, and the pioneering families pushed further into the surrounding bush. Techniques were developed for one farm worker to look after large numbers of sheep or cattle, a task made easier by the lack of predators. Teams of working dogs were essential, to extend the directions of the stock handler well beyond his feet or voice range. Also essential were good fences and gates, made from long-lasting wire, timber, steel and concrete; as was good field drainage, to take away low-lying water and make outside stocking possible right through winter.

The genetic development of sheep and cattle has been aimed at easy-care, self-reliant animals which will spread out on the hills and seek their own grass, without requiring intensive shepherding. In recent times farmers have re-established shelter belts of trees along the fence lines to provide protection from wind, snow and sun. Reliable stock water supplies are necessary, usually involving pumps from natural watercourses to tanks and then to troughs. Stock handling facilities are essential, such as yards, cattle and deer crushes and shearing sheds. Where possible these were designed so that one person with working dogs could corral, treat and release large numbers of animals without causing them undue stress. Animal care like hoof paring, lice prevention, shearing, castration and horn removal has always been important, so purpose-built facilities have been developed. Animal health treatments are also routine, although they are trending towards preventative rather than curative. Livestock may require mineral and vitamin supplements, along with internal and external parasite treatments, and the trend is towards easy application methods.

PASTURE GRAZING

In New Zealand, pastures are based on ryegrass and clover species, creating a wonderful grass and legume plant association for grazing animals. The early settlers sowed grasses like timothy, cocksfoot and browntop which would grow in low-fertility sites. But on these pastures it was not possible to run more than two sheep to the hectare and farmers needed to run more animals to be able to make a living from produce sales and get beyond self-sufficiency. From the early part of the twentieth century, plant breeders developed what has been called New Zealand's 'grassland revolution'. They wanted to breed species which extended the growing season and produced more palatable feed with higher energy levels. New perennial ryegrass and clover varieties were developed, with much higher productivity, followed by other improved ryegrasses, legumes, grazing herbs and forage brassicas.

In New Zealand the basic assumption is that standing feed should be available all year round, which the animals harvest themselves, avoiding the costs of supplementary feeding. What surpluses of pasture are available during the spring peak growing season are often cut for hay or silage, stored and then fed out during times of feed shortage. However many farms adjust their stocking rates to ensure that animals can go through the winter using just the banked-up standing feed, a practice called all-grass wintering. Break feeding or strip grazing is usually necessary to ration the pasture to animals, and prevent them from feeding inefficiently, trampling on good grass and 'cherry picking' only the best stuff.

Single-wire electric fences are run across the paddock, restricting animals to a pre-determined part of the available feed. The power fence is then moved each day, to supply some fresh pasture. The animals get into what is called a 'rotation' round paddocks during the winter and spring, so that by the time they return to any paddock, or part thereof, the grass has grown again. The concept of these power fences was a New Zealand invention in the 1930s, and they have been further developed and sold all round the world. An entire farm can now be controlled by one energiser, which delivers enough voltage to shock animals, but not enough current to do them any harm.

DAIRYING

The New Zealand dairy industry leads the world in efficient, low-cost milk production and its organisation is the envy of many countries. In the late 1800s farmers with a few cows started mechanically separating their milk into whey, which was fed to pigs, and cream, which was stored in cans and taken to a nearby dairy factory to be made into butter and cheese. There were hundreds of these small factories all over the country in dairying regions like Northland, Waikato, Taranaki, Manawatu, Nelson and Southland.

As herds became bigger and the roads became better for the national fleet of dairy tankers, dairy factories amalgamated until today there are less than 30, owned by just three companies. One of these, Fonterra Co-operative Group, owns 95 per cent of the export industry and is one of the five biggest dairy companies in the world. Fonterra now takes in 13 billion litres of fresh milk annually and makes whole milk and skim milk powders, butter, cheese, casein and other products to sell in more than 100 countries. The annual turnover of the company is $12 billion, which is about 10 per cent of New Zealand's gross domestic product. It has 13,000 farmer-shareholders, who have capital of over $500,000 each on average tied up in the giant company. The dairy industry is the technological leader of New Zealand's pastoral farming industries because of its size, its research effort and the technical demands for herd management, fertiliser use, water reticulation and milk harvesting.

SHEEP FARMING

Over 150 years New Zealand has developed a very productive sheep industry aimed at prime lambs for meat consumption, and clean, white wool for apparel and home furnishings such as carpets and drapes. Some 40 breeds of sheep now exist, grouped into fine, medium and strong wool types, and prime lamb types, often called dual-purpose breeds. The most numerous breed is the New Zealand Romney dual-purpose, which grows a 5 kilogram fleece of strong wool, and produces single or twin lambs each year that can be reared to 15-20 kilogram carcases during the spring and summer months. Annual production from 30 million ewes is around 40 million lambs and 200,000 tonnes of clean wool.

Sheep used to outnumber humans by twenty to one, but a fall in the size of the sheep flock has brought that ratio back to ten to one. Travelling around the country, it is easy to see just how many sheep occupy the hill pastures. Prime lamb meat is one of the world's most valuable proteins, presented in many appetising ways in high-class restaurants. Sheep are shorn once or twice a year and their fleeces are baled, cleaned and manufactured into woollen clothing or hard-wearing attractive carpets. Wool processing technology came from the United Kingdom, has been refined in New Zealand and is now implemented in centres of excellence in Yorkshire (UK), Germany, Italy, Japan and China. New Zealand now earns

$1 billion a year from wool exporting and $2.5 billion from lamb meat exporting.

BEEF PRODUCTION

New Zealand earns $2.5 billion annually from exports of beef, mainly to the United States and Asian countries. The beef herd is founded on two British breeds, Angus and Hereford, which have proven their hardiness and productivity on hill country pastures. Now the cows are often mated with European breeds like Simmental and Charolais, to produce faster-growing, larger crossbred steers and heifers. Beef production also owes much to the dairy industry, because surplus male calves are reared on milk powder mixed with water and then stocked in the paddocks to mature on grass to a killable size of around 300 kilograms carcase weight. About half of that weight is beef, which is lean, iron-rich and very nutritious. Because New Zealand cattle run outside all their lives, our beef production is characterised as 'grass-fed', in contrast to cattle in Australia, Japan, North America and Europe which are usually finished on feed supplements containing grain, producing a fattier, more marbled beef. All beef is aged and conditioned before retail sale for enhanced eating qualities.

HORTICULTURE

Abundant fruit and vegetables grow in warmer, sheltered regions of the country, like Bay of Islands, Bay of Plenty, Hawkes Bay, Horowhenua, Marlborough and Nelson. Total exports of fruit and vegetables now earn $2.2 billion annually, with a further $1 billion worth consumed domestically. New Zealand has developed many technological advances in fruit growing, like trellises for kiwifruit, passionfruit and cherries, or central leader growing forms for apples and stonefruit. Many orchards now limit the numbers of sprays applied through a system known as integrated pest management (IPM). This allows the pests to form sustainable populations, balanced by 'good' bugs as predators, and insecticides are only applied when pests get out of balance. Monitoring devices using pheromones to attract insects are essential tools.

The post-harvest grading, handling and storage of fruit is efficiently organised with some New Zealand inventions, and research and development work on new varieties and growing regimes is among the best in the world. New Zealand growers have come together to brand their fruit (Zespri in kiwifruit, Enza in apples) to differentiate their high-quality produce in world markets, contributing a great deal to New Zealand's image overseas. In most traded foods and commodities New Zealand will never be the biggest seller, but it aims to have the best quality.

The clean, green hills of New Zealand are a unique, untroubled environment for the low-input farming which is the envy of producers around the world.

OVERLEAF Mustering Hereford cattle at Birchwood Station on high country above the Ahuriri Valley, South Canterbury

LEFT Rolling pasture-covered hills, Balclutha, South Otago. The production base of New Zealand's world-leading sheep industry is found on easy hill country, cleared of native vegetation many years ago and planted in ryegrass and white clover pasture, where growth is ensured by mild temperatures, regular falls of rain and annual capital applications of phosphatic fertiliser and nitrogen. Ewes spend the whole year outside in the paddocks, mustered into sheep yards only for animal health treatments, weighing, shearing and pregnancy verification.

ABOVE Woolly Romney ewe with twin lambs on Hillview Farm, North Canterbury. Within four months these spring lambs will grow to 30 kg each and be ready for slaughter, processing and exporting to high-priced markets. Ewe fertility, lamb growth rates and meat qualities are among the best in the world, produced by New Zealand's temperate climate.

OVERLEAF Dairy farming, Delvin Farm, Taranaki. Flat farming land in districts with reliable rainfall is devoted to dairy farming, where milking cows feed on pastures with high energy levels.

OPPOSITE Dairy herd on Avondale Farm, Winton, Southland. The majority of New Zealand's 5 million dairy cows and heifers are a Holstein Friesian breed, favoured for their high volume of milk production, milk protein content and foraging ability.

ABOVE Feeding out hay on Tarlair Farm, Waikato. During colder months dairy cows are given a defined area of pasture each day, plus supplementary feed, conserved in spring as hay or silage when grass growth is too much for the cows to eat.

LEFT Farmers and livestock auctioneers on the rails of pens at Taumarunui saleyards. Dairy and beef cattle are bought and sold at weekly sales to obtain new breeding stock, dispose of finished animals or to reduce stock numbers because pasture feed conditions are tight.

Barley fields in the Lyalldale area, near Timaru, South Canterbury

LEFT Wheat harvesting at Woodlands, Temuka, South Canterbury. New Zealand produces less than half of the wheat supplies it needs for bread making, and the millers' silos are topped up from Australia. ABOVE More wheat harvesting, this time in the Methven area of Canterbury. The combine harvester discharges into the tractor-drawn bin while continuing to strip the wheat grains.

ABOVE Sheep mustering at Kahumingi, near Masterton, Wairarapa. Flocks of 30 million ewes and 25 million lambs are processed for export annually, earning $2.5 billion for lamb meat and $1 billion for wool. Early British settlers in the 1800s took English and Scottish sheep management methods and adapted them for New Zealand conditions. In the past decade, driven by exotic sheep imports like the Finn and Texel from Europe, sheep industry productivity has increased by 4 per cent annually. This is a compounded rate of growth not matched by any other sector of the New Zealand economy. The same weight of lamb meat each year is now produced by fewer than half the number of ewes in the 1970s, when there were 20 sheep for every person.

RIGHT Te Mata Peak, Hawkes Bay.
PREVIOUS PAGES Mt Ruapehu, the highest mountain in the North Island, photographed from near Waiouru where rolling downs are covered with grazing sheep.

LEFT Shearing a Merino ram at Rakaia, Canterbury. Shearing is one of the hardest jobs in New Zealand agriculture, performed by skilled professional shearers or farmers who do their own sheep. Sheep grow fleeces of 5 kg or more each year, which must be shorn before they become too heavy and weigh the sheep down to the point of exhaustion. Farmers receive between $3 and $10 a kilogram of wool, depending on fineness and quality, which then must be cleaned or scoured, combed to remove seeds and align the fibres, spun into yarn, dyed and manufactured into floor coverings or clothes.

ABOVE Shearing in a four-stand shed at Kahumingi, Masterton, Wairarapa. Woolly sheep are kept in pens behind the shearers, who work on elevated platforms so the wool handlers, in front, can gather the shorn fleeces without bending down. OPPOSITE Shearing on Mt Nicholas Station, Otago. Shorn wool must be sorted or classed into different lines of types and qualities. The first step is to throw the fleece on to the sorting table.

Sunflower crop, near Oamaru, North Otago

29

LEFT A mixed-breed dairy herd, Te Awamutu, Waikato. Many New Zealand dairy farmers now run mixed-breed or crossbred dairy cows, to combine the greater milk-volume production of the Holstein Friesian (black and white) with the greater milk fat production of the Jersey breed (light brown). Crossbreeds have a uniform dark brown/black coat colour and are called the 'Kiwi cow'. These are efficient hybrids without the large body size and bigger maintenance feed requirement of the Holstein Friesian.

ABOVE A beautiful Jersey cow. The second most numerous breed of dairy cow in New Zealand, Jerseys are favoured for their compact size, high milk fat content and good nature. What they might lack in milk volume compared with Holstein Friesians, they make up in stocking rate, with more cows to the hectare and hence more milk production per hectare.

PREVIOUS PAGES Farmer and dogs, alone on Dalrachney Station, Otago.

LEFT Merinos cross a fast-flowing tributary of the Jollie River on Braemar Station, Mackenzie Country, Canterbury, with help from a shepherd.

ABOVE Merino sheep among the tussock grasses on Braemar Station. Hardy, fine-woolled Merino sheep were the first to be introduced to New Zealand, in 1813, but are now confined to the South Island high country. Three million Merinos produce long white wool which is very suitable for apparel use, and fetches prices three or four times higher than strong wool. However Merino ewes usually produce a small, slow-growing lamb each year, which is not very suitable for meat markets.

Winter snow at Castle Hill Station, Canterbury, with the Torlesse Range in the background

LEFT Feeding out for sheep in the snow in the Ahuriri Valley, South Canterbury. Sheep are well able to cope with cold weather and snow, provided they can break the snow and ice cover with their hooves to reach pasture. Farmers feed out hay or silage as supplementary fodder until the snow melts.

ABOVE Sheep enjoy supplementary fodder at Castle Hill Station, Canterbury. Sunshine warms the sheep and melts the snow, which will usually hang around for a few days at most on the flats.

OVERLEAF White-out winter conditions at Dunstan Downs, Dunstan Range, Otago, when the shepherd needs to watch over his sheep. Heavy snowfalls may call for the shepherd to 'rake' out trails to fresh feed for the sheep by stamping down thick snow.

ABOVE Sheep dog in control, Loburn, North Canterbury. Sheep dogs are the unsung heroes of farming in New Zealand; willing workers who expect only a meat or biscuits meal, water, a warm bed and a pat on the head for a job well done. Farmers would be lost without the ability of their dogs to round up sheep and cattle in response to the handler's voice or whistle. 'Eye' dogs are silent workers, using anticipation, speed and the occasional nip to make the livestock obey. 'Heading' dogs push the sheep or cattle in front of them, using 'noise', or repeated barking.

Shepherds train their dogs to recognise many different commands, such as to go left or right, cast away, come to or go away, stop, sit, walk up and speak up.

RIGHT A sheep mob on the move, directed by a horseman and his two dogs, on Erewhon Station, Taihape, Rangitikei. Sheep will keep together when moving, but the dogs are there to push them along and round up strays.

PREVIOUS PAGES The big pastures of a hill country sheep and cattle farm, Taumarunui, King Country.

Beef cattle farm, Waitomo, Waikato

LEFT Te Kouma Harbour on Coromandel Peninsula, with Rangipukea Island. On the horizon across the Firth of Thames can be seen the hills around Auckland, New Zealand's largest city, which is located on the Hauraki Gulf, north of the firth. The cloud formations above the hills are a good example of why Maori called the country Aotearoa, the Land of the Long White Cloud. Such beautiful coastline and access to good fishing and pleasure-boating waters make any remaining seaside farms highly sought after, with the larger ones valued at tens of millions of dollars. In what is called the golden crescent, a 500-kilometre stretch of coastline from the Bay of Islands in Northland right round the north-eastern coast of the North Island, past Auckland and Coromandel to the Bay of Plenty, land values for coastal properties are very high. It can make those farms uneconomic as productive units, so owners sell for subdivision and the land is largely lost to farming.

ABOVE Farm buildings near Fantail Bay, Coromandel Peninsula. An example of a shearing shed and yards disused since the property was sold for subdivision into building blocks or lifestyle farms.

ABOVE Hayward green kiwifruit, hanging on the vine in Te Puke, Bay of Plenty. New Zealand commercialised the Chinese gooseberry from the 1970s onwards, calling it kiwifruit, a new fruit which has spread around the world. Exports of kiwifruit through the grower-owned Zespri company are now worth $1 billion a year.

RIGHT Newly-planted kiwifruit seedlings being trained along wires. Most new plantings are the Zespri Gold variety, a lovely sweet yellow fruit which commands a premium price over the green Hayward. Zespri has licensed the area of Gold grown here and overseas, to ensure steady market development, without the boom and bust which beset the green variety in the 1980s.

LEFT AND ABOVE Vineyards on Waiheke Island, Hauraki Gulf, Auckland. Just 30 minutes by fast ferry from New Zealand's largest city of over 1 million people lies Waiheke Island, with its idyllic lifestyle of sheltered coves and sandy beaches. More than a dozen small wineries specialise in top quality red wines, with good restaurants and displays of local art and crafts. Waiheke retains a relaxed holiday feel although it is now home to many Auckland commuters. New Zealand's wine-making industry has grown considerably in climatically favoured regions like Hawkes Bay, Wairarapa, Marlborough, Nelson and Central Otago. More than 18,000 ha is planted under grapes, with the highest volume variety, chardonnay, and the flagship variety, sauvignon blanc, making up the bulk of production. Sauvignon blanc has a reputation at home and overseas for its exuberant flavours and is acknowledged as the best in the world in this variety. New Zealand's vintages are now over 100,000 tonnes of grapes harvested, and exports have risen above 40 million litres, earning about $300 million.

OVERLEAF Hereford cattle at Linton, near Palmerston North.

53

Wharekauhau Station, Palliser Bay, Wairarapa

LEFT Cattle graze the shores of Lake Taupo, New Zealand's largest lake, formed in the crater left by a huge volcanic explosion. The pumice and volcanic dust left covering the land have low fertility and suffer from a cobalt deficiency, which until the 1930s resulted in the mystery 'bush sickness' which knocked livestock. When the cobalt problem was discovered and solved, farming expanded through the Central Plateau region, in the middle of the North Island. However much of the region was planted in *Pinus radiata* trees for forestry.

ABOVE Musterers at Opotiki, Bay of Plenty. On extensive farms fringed by bush, stockmen still use horses and dogs to round up cattle rather than farm motorbikes, trucks or tractors.

Lake Coleridge and the Craigieburn Range, Canterbury

LEFT Cattle yarding of Hereford cows and calves at Landsborough Station, Westland. The wild and wet West Coast region of the South Island lies in the shadow of the Southern Alps and contains bush-fringed farms remote from urban centres. Farmers practise extensive farming dictated by the seasons, with infrequent mustering of cattle and sheep, which are left to forage all year round.

ABOVE One of the most practical methods of rounding up cattle on Landsborough Station is to use a helicopter to spot the animals on pastures a long way from the homestead. The aircraft noise drives mobs into the open where musterers on horse-back take over. Helicopters are also used to capture wild deer with nets, and to take hunting, tramping and skiing parties to inaccessible areas of South Westland and Fiordland.

The flats and shallows of the lower river valleys on Landsborough Station provide the easiest route for stock movement.

The whole family takes to horseback to help muster cattle down from high pastures to the homestead and yards near the South Westland coast. Many dogs are required to push the mobs across the snow-fed rivers, like the Jackson pictured here.

ABOVE Stonefruit trees near Cromwell, Central Otago. Trained into vase shapes which provide maximum sunlight for the developing fruit, rows of apricot, nectarine, peach and cherry trees march across the lovely landscape of Central Otago, where about half of New Zealand's stonefruits are grown.

RIGHT Leaves turning yellow and snow-covered hills around Alexandra signal autumn in Central Otago. Cold winters with hard frosts are good for deciduous fruit trees, killing pests and diseases. In the summer, high sunlight hours in the region produce the best fruit, with good sugar levels and skin colours. However, dry summers also bring a need for irrigation so that trees thrive and bear good fruit (PREVIOUS PAGES). More than 500 growers of stonefruits on 3000 ha are organised into a promotion and regulation body called Summerfruit New Zealand, which publicises crop standards, technical issues and recipes. Exports total 2500 tonnes annually, mostly apricots and cherries. Stonefruits are technically demanding to grow, especially cherries, as fruit may blemish or split with rubbing damage or wet weather.

LEFT An apple orchard early in the season in Takaka Valley, Golden Bay, Nelson. Nelson province is the second-largest apple growing region, in a national pipfruit industry with annual export earnings of $500 million.

ABOVE Apple orchard in blossom at Havelock North, Hawkes Bay, the centre of the New Zealand apple industry. The world-leading apple breeding programme is carried out by HortResearch and backed by growers through the levies they pay on each carton of fruit. Braeburn, Royal Gala, Pacific Rose and Jazz varieties are among the results of research. Along with developing attractive new varieties, technical work goes into tree cultivation, orchard management and post-harvest storage conditions.

OPPOSITE Farmed deer behind two-metre-high fences in the Queenstown area of Otago. New Zealand pioneered the commercial farming of deer on pasture in the 1970s and remains the world's largest producer of farm-raised venison and velvet. Deer were introduced in the 1800s as game animals and found New Zealand bush and mountains to their liking, becoming a noxious animal pest for the damage they caused to native plants. Then demand for venison in Germany in the 1960s sparked an export industry based on shot and retrieved deer carcases. Entrepreneurial farmers started capturing live feral deer, using one-way gates on the margins of bush or nets fired from helicopters, and the red deer species proved to be quite adaptable to life behind fences on green pastures. There are now 2 million farmed deer and the management methods have spread to Australia, North America and Europe.

LEFT TOP Red deer hinds grazing peacefully at Loburn, North Canterbury. With control over their new livestock species, New Zealand deer farmers have built an industry worth more than $250 million in venison exports and $50 million in velvet exports annually.

LEFT BELOW An elk stag pictured at Te Anau, Southland. Larger stags, like this one with his magnificent head of velvet antler, are bred to red deer hinds to produce crossbred fawns which will grow faster to higher carcase weights. The velvet is harvested each year under local anaesthetic and sliced and powdered for human consumption, as a good source of iron and other nutrients.

ABOVE Beautiful Glentanner Station, on the Ben Ohau Range and the shore of Lake Pukaki, South Canterbury, looking across to the Southern Alps and Aoraki/Mt Cook, New Zealand's highest mountain (3754 m), in the centre.

LEFT A magnificent Merino ram at Haycocks Station, Marlborough, with the curly horns so characteristic of the breed, which is the world's oldest and most numerous. In New Zealand there are about 3 million Merinos, kept for their long, white, lustrous wool.

OPPOSITE Mustering Merino sheep at Glenrock Station, upper Rakaia Valley, Canterbury. The sheep must be brought down from the high country to lower, warmer pastures at the onset of winter.

OVERLEAF Sheep mustering by Glentanner Station along the Mount Cook Road, South Canterbury.

LEFT On of the most popular trips for tourists in New Zealand is the boat ride across Lake Wakatipu from Queenstown to Walter Peak Station on the historic coal-fired, steam-driven TSS *Earnslaw*. Once landed, they see demonstrations of farm life, including mustering on horseback and shearing.

ABOVE Woolshed and sheep on Mt Hutt Station, Canterbury, near to Mt Hutt ski-field and within a short driving distance of many farm tourism locations.

OVERLEAF Cattle grazing at Fox Glacier, Westland, in the shadow of the Southern Alps, near State Highway 6, a well-travelled scenic route from Haast Pass to Greymouth.

LEFT Rippon Vineyard, Lake Wanaka, Otago, with Ruby Island offshore. Central Otago, around Cromwell, Queenstown and Wanaka, has seen an explosion of grape growing in recent years. The conditions here are ideal for producing high quality pinot noir and riesling wines.

ABOVE Pinot noir grapes on the vine, Marlborough. Pinot noir is a difficult wine to make, and Central Otago is producing some of the best of this variety in the world.

Brancott Estate vineyard, Marlborough

LEFT Under a glowering sky and pale sunshine, in the aptly named Nightcaps area of Southland, ewes graze on a good cover of grass. The southernmost province of New Zealand has one of the biggest sheep populations, almost all dual-purpose breeds for lamb and wool production. Highly fertile ewes will produce twin lambs and rear them both to 30 kg live weight at weaning, three months after lambing, as well as producing 5 kg annually of good, strong white wool. That means the ewe is duplicating her own 60 kg body weight in a very productive spring period, earning income of perhaps $160 or more for the farm.
ABOVE A spring-born lamb only a few days old, well-covered with wool in case of late storms and already on a growth path of 300 grams per day through the first 3 months of life. Ewes are left alone to give birth, so as to ensure the selection of those good mothers who produce vigorous lambs.

Braemar Station, on Lake Pukaki, Mackenzie Country, Canterbury

LEFT Barry's Bay, near Akaroa, on Banks Peninsula, Canterbury. Hill-country farming here is influenced by the sea and the weather, which combine to create an equable climate well-suited for pastoral agriculture. Banks Peninsula has a style of farming and a history of settlement which is unique in Canterbury, having been heavily influenced by the pre-European Maori, Ngai Tahu, and the early French settlers at Akaroa. Canterbury is one of the biggest farming provinces, with a wide range of crops, livestock and enterprises.

ABOVE Springs Junction, Buller, Westland, where sheep graze under the lee of the Southern Alps. The high mountain range collects rain clouds and creates a warm fohn wind pattern on its easterly side, which often leads to summer drought.

ABOVE Sheep on the move in the Awatere Valley, Marlborough. The demand for horticultural land is now reaching far up the Wairau and Awatere valleys and scenes with livestock are becoming less common in Marlborough. One weak or orphaned lamb has hitched a ride on the back of the farm bike.

RIGHT Current Bay and D'Urville Island in the Marlborough Sounds, at the northern end of the South Island. Marlborough is a geologically diverse province, which contains sheep and cattle farming, dairying, grape growing and wine making and aquaculture, mainly greenshell mussels farmed in the clear waters of the Sounds. Marlborough sauvignon blanc wine is considered to be the best in the world, leading to a land rush around the provincial capital, Blenheim, for vineyard development.

OPPOSITE A predominantly Jersey cow herd near Paihiatua, in the Tararua district of the lower North Island, which is strong dairying country, with prolific grass growth, regular rains and good animal health conditions. This means high milk production levels and an extended dairy season of up to 300 days.

LEFT ABOVE Milking in a rotary dairy shed, Westland, where cows learn to walk into the bails as the empty stalls pass in front of them, presenting their udders to the operator standing in the surrounding 'pit'. The teats are washed and the cups applied. Milking takes place as the cows circle around the shed, then the cups drop off automatically when milk flow finishes, and the cows back off the platform to walk out to the paddocks. The rotary platform concept came from a Taranaki dairy farmer and when perfected by applied engineers it spread quickly through New Zealand's dairying regions, and then overseas. Refinements such as automatic cup removal and milk metering have been introduced to reduce the number of farm workers needed during each milking. Now the labour requirement in the on-farm part of the dairy industry has fallen to two full-time farmers per average herd of 300 cows, with two milkings a day.

LEFT BELOW The dairy company milk tanker collects from a farm vat in Westland. At the peak of the dairy production season, milk tankers are continuously on the move from farm to factory, so that each farm's milk production is collected every day or every second day. The annual production of 13 billion litres goes into more than 20 big dairy factories around the country, to be made into milk powders, butter, cheese and casein before export to more than 100 countries. The dairy industry earns 20 per cent of New Zealand's annual export revenues.

LEFT Beef cattle on Summerlee Station, Hawkes Bay. Easier hill country throughout New Zealand is used for beef cattle farming, usually in combination with sheep farming. The industry is founded on two British breeds, Angus and Hereford, and when these two are crossed the progeny often comes out with distinctive white faces and a solid dark coat colour. In the past 40 years exotic European breeds like Simmental and Charolais have been used in breeding combinations with the base herds, to produce bigger offspring.

ABOVE Beef calves with a dairy influence, sourced from the huge dairy industry and then reared for their meat production, not milk.

OVERLEAF A Holstein Friesian dairy cattle herd at Penshurst farm, near Palmerston North, Manawatu.

LEFT Productive North Island hill-country farming near Tokirima, Taumarunui, King Country. New Zealand's geologically young soils are not naturally fertile enough for agriculture and need large quantities of fertiliser to lift the nitrogen, phosphorus and potassium levels, with lime to raise the pH. The practice of sowing white clover with ryegrass also provides a huge boost to soil nitrogen through the rhizobial fixation process in root nodules.

ABOVE Fertiliser spreading by aeroplane, a practice called topdressing, was pioneered in New Zealand after World War Two using surplus military aeroplanes. It is now carried out over huge tracts of hill country which are inaccessible by ground spreaders, using Fletcher planes specially built by Pacific Aerospace Corporation, Hamilton. OVERLEAF Erewhon Station, Taihape, Rangitikei.

LEFT Sheep grazing on rolling downs near Fairlie, South Canterbury. Extensive sheep farming has ewes set-stocked in large paddocks for long periods, during which they forage for feed and drink from water troughs, filled from tanks located on the tops of hills.

ABOVE Hay bales, Central Otago. Surplus pasture during the high-growth spring period is cut and left to dry before being rolled into big round bales secured with twine or netting. These are then collected and stacked as conserved fodder, to be fed out again to livestock in periods of low pasture growth.

OVERLEAF The Canterbury Plains in all their patchwork glory, showing paddocks in different stages of cultivation. The Rakaia River (right) runs down from the Southern Alps in the background, with Mt Hutt prominent right centre.

LEFT Large-scale market gardening, Oamaru, North Otago. Irrigation boosts vegetable growth in time for peak domestic market demand.

ABOVE Spreading fertiliser with a tractor at Fairlie, South Canterbury.

OVERLEAF A late autumn sunrise over the Waipara district of North Canterbury.